THE NINETIES

PART THREE

Production: Ulf Klenfeldt
Cover Design by Headline Publicity Limited

Published 2000

International Music Publications Limited
Griffin House 161 Hammersmith Road London W6 8BS England

ANGELS

Words and Music by
ROBBIE WILLIAMS and GUY CHAMBERS

C#m7
4fr
A
D
un - fold.
So when I'm
ly-ing in my bed
thoughts
A/C#
A
E
D
A/C#
run-ning through my head
and I
feel that love is
dead,
I'm lov-ing an-gels in-stead.
E
B
C#m
4fr
And through it
all
she of-fers me pro-tec - tion,
a lot of love and af-fec-
A
Asus2
E
B
tion
whe-ther I'm right or
wrong.
And down the wa - ter-fall
wher-ev-er
it may take

C#m
4fr
A
Asus2
E/G#
me, I know that life won't break me, when I come to call she won't for-sake
F#m
Dadd9
A/C#
to Coda
E
me, I'm lov-ing an-gels in-stead.
Asus2
A
C#m/A
4fr
When I'm feel-ing weak and my pain walks down a one way street,
B
E
I look a-bove and I know I'll al-ways be blessed

Asus2
A
C#m/A
4fr
B
D
— with love, —
and as the feel-ing grows —
she brings
A/C#
A
E
Dadd9
A/C#
E
D.S al Coda
flesh to my bones
and when love is dead,
I'm lov-ing an-gels in-stead.
And through is all
CODA
E
Bm
F#m/A
E
Bm
F#m/A
1.
E

2.

E/G♯ B C♯m

And through it all ___ she of-fers me_ pro-tec - tion, a lot of love and af-fec-

A Asus2 E B

- tion whe-ther I'm right or wrong. And down the wa - ter-fall ___ wher-ev-er it_ may take

C♯m 4fr A Asus2 E/G♯

___ me, I know that life won't break_ me,_ when I come to call she won't for-sake

rit.

F♯m Dadd9 A/C♯ E

___ me, I'm lov - ing an - gels in - stead.

AIN'T THAT A LOT OF LOVE

Words and Music by
WILLIA DEAN PARKER
and HOMER BANKS

Fm7
A♭m9
A♭maj7
E♭maj7
To Coda
lot of love for one heart to hold? (2.) If the
bees on - ly knew how sweet you are ba - by, they would seal up their ho - ney - comb.
lips are so sweet. Ho - ney you're my ev - 'ry
need. You've got a smile so red. A
If the birds could hear how sweet your voice is, they would
tight - en up their song.
love like yours I just can't com - pare.
Ain't that a lot of love

1.
2.
A♭m9
A♭maj7
E♭maj7
for one heart — to hold? —
(3.) Your
Ain't that — a
Fm7
lot of love
for one heart — to hold?
Sax.
D.%. al Coda
(4.) If the

Coda
A♭maj7
E♭maj7
Fm7
A♭m9
Ain't that a lot of love for
one heart to hold?
One heart to hold?
Fm9
A♭
E♭
Ain't that a lot of love
for one heart to
hold?
Ain't that a lot of love
8va

N.C.
for one heart_to hold?
Oh,
(8va)
loco
oh that's a lot of love.
Sure_e-nough got a lot_
_of love
for one heart to hold.
E♭m
G♭
A♭
E♭m
Repeat ad lib. to fade
One heart to hold.
Oh, hold.

BEAUTIFUL STRANGER

Words and Music by
MADONNA CICCONE
and WILLIAM ORBIT

C♯7sus
C♯7
C♯7sus
for me.
I've had the taste for dan - ger.
Verses 2 & 3:
C♯7
C♯7sus
C♯7
2. If I'm smart, then I'll run a - way.
3. If I'm smart, then I'll run a - way.
C♯7sus
C♯7
C♯7sus
But I'm not, so I'll guess I'll stay. Heav - en for - bid.
But I'm not, so I'll guess I'll stay. Have - n't you heard?
C♯7
C♯7sus
C♯7
I'll take my chance on a beau - ti - ful strang - er.
I fell in love with a beau - ti - ful strang - er.

Bridge:
B
A
1. I looked in - to your eyes, and my world
2. I looked in - to your face, my heart was
3. I looked in - to your eyes, and my world
C#7sus
C#7
came tum - bl - ing down.
danc - in' all o - ver the place.
came tum - bl - ing down.
B
A
You're the dev - il in dis - guise. That's why I'm
I'd like to change my point of view, if I could
You're the dev - il in dis - guise. That's why I'm
C#7sus
C#7
sing - ing this song.
just for - get a - bout you.
sing - ing this song to you.

Chorus:
F♯
E
B
To know you is to love you.
C♯7sus
C♯7
C♯7sus
To Coda
You're ev - 'ry-where I go.
And ev - 'ry - bod - y
1.
C♯7
F♯
knows.
To love you
E
B
C♯7sus
is to be part of you.
I paid for you with

C#7
C#7sus
C#7
tears
and swal-lowed all my pride.
E
B
F#
A
C#7sus
Da da da da da da da da da da da da da.
Beau - ti - ful
C#7
E
B
F#
A
strang - er.
Da da da da da da da da da da da da da.
C#7
C#7sus
Beau - ti - ful strang - er.

C♯7
2.
C♯7
D.S.𝄋 al Coda
knows.
𝄌 Coda
C♯7
C♯7sus
knows.
I paid for you with
C♯7
C♯7sus
C♯7
tears
and swal-lowed all my pride.
E
B
F♯
A
C♯7sus
Da da da da da da da da da da da da da.
Beau - ti - ful

C♯7
E
B
F♯
A
strang - er.
Da da da da da da da da da da da da da.
C♯7
C♯7sus
Beau - ti - ful strang - er.
C♯7
C♯7sus
C♯7
Repeat ad lib. and fade

AS TIME GOES BY

Words and Music by HERMAN HUPFELD

Ebm7
Ab7
Db
Ebm7
Edim
Db6
still say "I love you," on that you can re-ly; no
Eb7
Ab7
Ebm7
Ab7
Db6
mat-ter what the fu-ture brings as time goes by.
Db7
Gb6
Bb7
Moon-light and love songs, nev-er out of date,
2º Instrumental ad lib.
Ebm7
Bbdim
Db/F
hearts full of pas-sion, jea-lou-sy and hate; wo-man needs man and

E♭7
A♭6
A♭dim
A♭7
man must have his mate, that no-one can de - ny.
Instrumental ends 2°
It's
E♭m7
A♭7
E♭m7
A♭7
D♭
E♭m7
Edim
still the same old sto - ry, a fight for love and glo - ry, a case of do or die.
D♭
E♭7
1.
A♭
B♭7
E♭m7add11
A♭6
The world will al - ways wel - come lov - ers as time goes by.
D♭6
E♭7
D♭7
2.
A♭7
B♭9
E♭m7add11
A♭7add13
D♭6
lov - ers as time goes by.
8va

BELIEVE

Words and Music by BRIAN HIGGINS, STUART MCLENNAN, PAUL BARRY, STEPHEN TORCH, MATT GRAY and TIM POWELL

C
F
talk - ing to you. It's so sad that you're leav -
turn - ing back. I need time to move
Am
Bb
- ing, takes time to be - lieve it, but af - ter all is
on I need love to feel strong, 'cause I've had time to
C
said and done, you're going to be the lone - ly one, oh.
think it through, and may - be I'm too good for you, oh.
F
C
Gm
3fr
Bb
Do you be - lieve in life af - ter love? I can feel

F
C
Gm
3fr
Dm
— some-thing in - side — me say, — I real-ly don't think you're strong — e - nough, no. —
F
C
Gm
3fr
B♭
Do you be - lieve — in life — af-ter love? — I can feel
F
C
Gm
3fr
Dm
— some-thing in - side — me say, — I real-ly don't think you're strong — e - nough, no. —
Dm
C
But I know — that I'll — get through this, —

Dm
'cause I know that I am strong.
C
Bb
I don't need you a-ny-more, I don't need
C
Bb
you a-ny-more, Oh, I don't need you a-ny-more,
Gm7
3fr
C
no, I don't need you a-ny-more.

F
C
Gm
3fr
B♭
Do you be - lieve in life af - ter love?
I can feel
Am7
Dm
some - thing in - side me say,
I real - ly don't think you're strong e - nough, no.
repeat to fade

BOOTIE CALL

Words and Music by KARL GORDON
and SHAZNAY LEWIS

Fm
C7
Bring it on, bring it, bring it on now. Bring it on, bring it, bring it on now.
(Boo - tie call) (It's just a boo-tie call)
Fm
C
Bring it on, bring it, bring it on now. Bring it on, bring it, bring it on now.
(Boo - tie call) (It's just a boo-tie call)
Fm
C7
To Coda
Bring it on, bring it, bring it on now. Bring it on, bring it, bring it on now.
(Boo - tie call) (It's just a boo-tie call)
Fm
C
1. Nev - er stop giv - ing good love 'cause that's what I call you for.
(Verse 2 see block lyric)

Fm
C
Nev- er stop ba- by give it up 'cause I know where it came from, you got more.
Fm
C
I like play - ing games and if it's all the same
Fm
C
3
you can bring it on with the rough stuff and give me young love, I don't want to be tame.
Fm
C
3
I need a man to be a real man now, in ord - er what I got in store,

Fm
C7
al-ways fin-ish what you start ba - by and al-ways hav-in' you beg for more.
Fm
C
You know I wan-na be dig-gy down boy, but I don't get a - round,
Fm
C7
D.%. al Coda
Jim-my hitched a ride in your pock-et I lock him in your wal-let, it's just a boo-tie call.
Coda
Fm
C
Fm
C7

Verse 2:
I'm keen on you what is baby
Some things are always good to have
You never let me down
I'm always happy when you make me laugh
But don't try to find
This heart of mine
Emotions don't come into my head
So don't be misled, my heart doesn't need to be bled.

Only trying to be smart babe
Don't need the rollercoaster ride
I've been and seen and done it all yeah
Don't want you messing with my mind
So don't be a fool
Keep this as your number one rule:
Good loving's not always from the heart
You got to be smart, stay just the way you are.

C'EST LA VIE

Words and Music by EDELE LYNCH,
KEANY LYNCH, LINDSAY ARMOU,
SINEAD O'CARROLL, RAY HEDGES,
MARTIN BRANNIGAN and TRACEY ACKERMAN

Don't be shy, straight-en up your tie. Get down from your tree-house sit-tin' in the sky,
I wan-na know just what I do. Is it ve-ry big, is there room for two?
I got a house with a win-dows and doors, I'll show you mine if you'll show me yours.
Em7
A7
D11
fr5
G
D/F♯
Got-ta let me in. Hey. Let the fun be-gin. Hey.

Em7
A7
Cm7
fr3
I'm the wolf to - day, hey I'll huff, I'll puff, I'll
G
C
D
Dsus4/2
fr2
huff, I'll puff, I'll blow you a - way.
Say you will, say you won't, say you'll do what I don't. Say you're true,
say to me c'est la vie. Say you will, say you won't, say you'll do
what I don't, say you're true, say to me c'est la vie.
1.
2. Do you

2.
G
D
D sus4/2
fr2
D
N.C.
c'est la vie.
Na na na na na na.
A
D
A
E
Ha ha na na na hey.
Na na na oh.
Na na na hey.

A
D
E
Esus4/2
Ha ha ha ha. Say you will,
say you won't, say you'll do what I don't. Say you're true, say to me, wan-na say
c'est la vie. Say you will, say you won't, say you'll do
what I don't. Say you're true, say to me,

Verse 2:
Do you play with the girls
Play with the boys?
Do you ever get lonely
Playing with your toy?
We can talk
We can sing
I'll be the queen
And you'll be the king.
Hey boy, in your tree
Throw down your ladder
Make-a room for me
I gotta a house with a windows and doors
I'll show you mine if you'll show me yours.

Gotta let me in *etc.*

CRUSH

Words and Music by BERNY COSGROVE,
KEVIN CLARK, ANDY GOLDMARK
and MARK MUELLAR

Verse:
C♯m
B/C♯
F♯m/C♯
1. See you blow-in' me a kiss, it does-n't take a sci-en-tist to un-der-stand what's go-ing on, ba-
raising my a-dren-a-line, your bang-in' on a heart of tin. Please don't make too much of it, ba-
G♯m/C♯
C♯m
B/C♯
by. If you see some-thing in my eye, let's not o-ver an-a-lyze.
by. Say the word for-ev-er-more, that's not what I'm look-ing for.
F♯m/C♯
G♯m/C♯
Don't go too deep with it, ba - by.
All I can com - mit to is may - be.
C♯m
B/C♯
So let it be what it-'ll be. Don't make a fuss and get cra-

F♯m/C♯
G♯m/C♯
C♯m
zy o - ver you and me.
Here's what I do, I play it loose,
B/C♯
F♯m/C♯
G♯m/C♯
not like we have a date with des - ti - ny.
It's
Chorus:
C♯m
F♯m
A maj7
G♯m7
F♯m7
just a lit - tle crush, not like I faint ev - 'ry time we
B
C♯m
F♯m
touch. It's just some lit - tle thing, not like ev -

Amaj7
G♯m7
F♯m7
B
C♯m
'ry-thing I do depends on you.
Sha la la la.
1.
Sha la la la.
2. It's
2.
Bridge:
B/C♯
Va-nil-la skies.
A/C♯
B/C♯
C♯m
white pick-et fenc - es in your eyes.
A

B/C♯
C♯m
vi - sion of you___ and me.___
It's
C♯m
F♯m
Amaj7
G♯m7
F♯m7
just a lit - tle crush, not like I faint ev - 'ry time we
(Vocal ad lib.)
B
C♯m
F♯m
touch.___ It's just some lit - tle thing, not like ev -
Amaj7
G♯m7
F♯m7
B
Repeat ad lib. and fade
'ry - thing I do___ de - pends on you.___

DAYZ LIKE THAT

Words and Music by ALISTAIR TENNANT,
KARL GORDON and MICHELLE ESCOFFERY

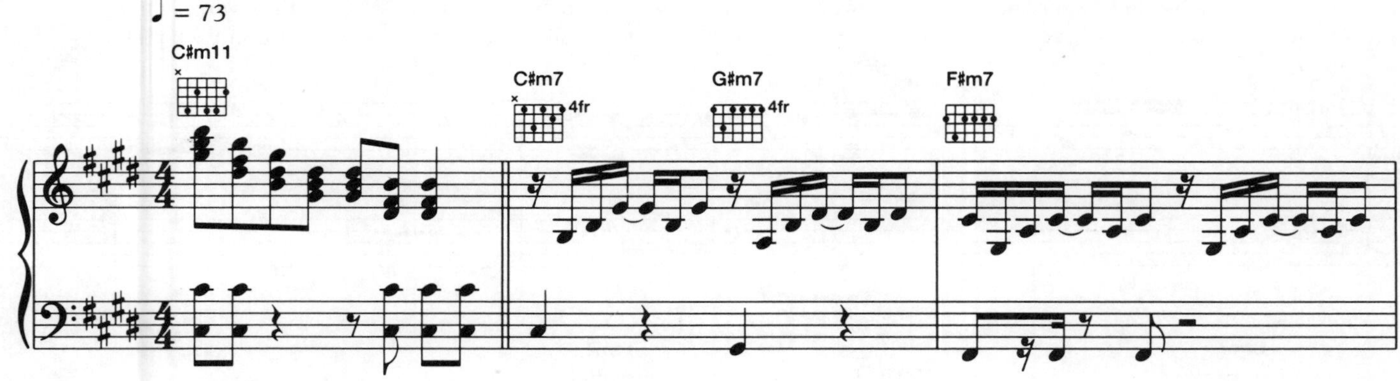

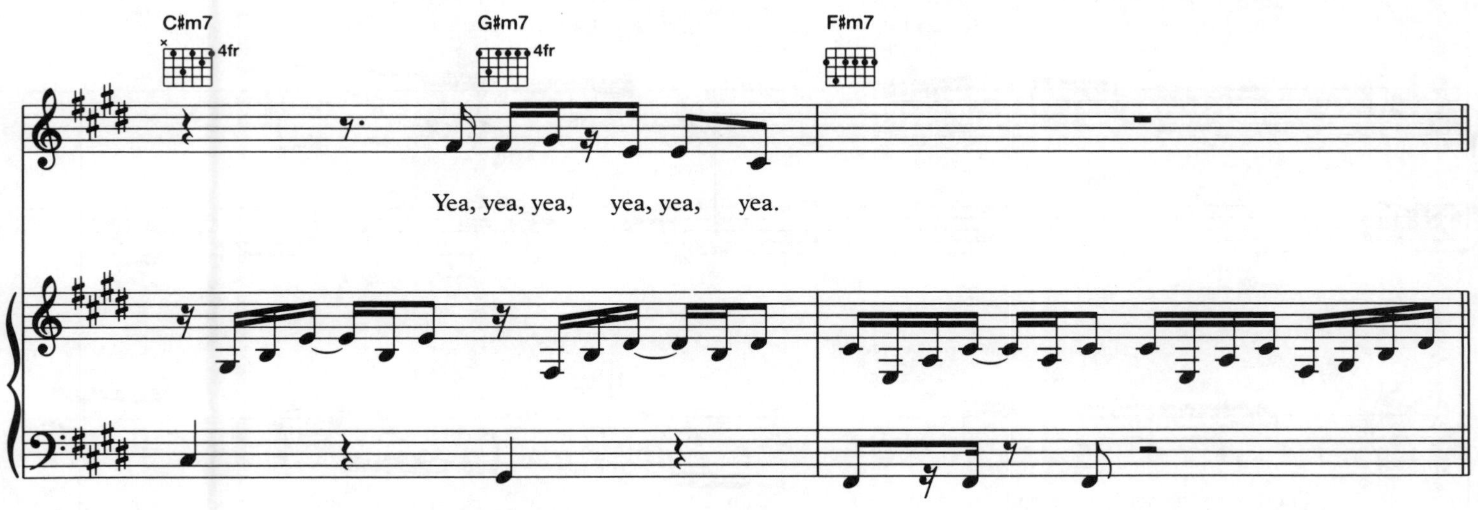

C#m7
4fr
G#m7
4fr
F#m7
You've had some time to live with the mes - ses that you made.
I should have nev - er just let you walk a - way and not ex - plain.
Not trying to say I'm per - fect push come to shove I'm worth it.
But I'm a it no, no, I had to get o - ver it.
There were things you've had to deal with but it's al - right 'cause we're still tied, yea, yea. I
It made me strong - er with - in there's a les - son here, hope you learn from it, ooh, yea.
can't be - lieve you're back a - gain af - ter all you put me through.

F#m7
Ev - en though I'm still you're friend I don't want to be with you. Re -
C#m7
4fr
G#m7
4fr
F#m7
- mem-ber when days_ were like that, I was lov-ing you ev-ery time_ you loved back, and now you're
C#m7
4fr
G#m7
4fr
F#m7
tell-ing me that_ you miss that, bet you feel lone - ly_____ but it's like_ that. Do you re -
C#m7
4fr
G#m7
4fr
F#m7
- mem-ber when days_ were like that, I was lov-ing you ev-ery-time_ you loved back, and now you're

C#m7
4fr
G#m7
4fr
F#m7
tell-ing me that you miss that, bet you feel lone - ly that you lost me ba - by,
C#m7
4fr
G#m7
4fr
F#m7
yea.
C#m7
4fr
G#m7
4fr
F#m7
F#m7
C#m7
4fr
We can be friends but not lov - ers, ah, ooh, ooh, ooh, oh, oh,

F#m7
1.
C#m7
G#m7
D#m7
F#maj7/A#
4fr
got to be one_ not the oth - er,
bet-ter un-der-stand I'm not play-ing.
2.
C#m7
bet-ter un-der-stand I'm not play-ing,
play-ing,
play-ing.
Do you re -
C#m7
G#m7
F#m7
- mem - ber when days were like that,
I was lov-ing
you ev-ery time_ you loved back,
and now you're
C#m7
G#m7
F#m7
tell-ing me that_ you miss that,
bet you feel lone - ly_____ but it's like_ that.
Do you re -

C#m7
4fr
G#m7
4fr
F#m7
-mem-ber when days were like that, I was lov-ing you ev-ery time_ you loved back, and now you're
C#m7
4fr
G#m7
4fr
1.
F#m7
tell-ing me that_ you miss that, bet you feel lone - ly_ that you lost_ me. Do you re -
2.
F#m7
C#m7
4fr
G#m7
4fr
_ ly_ that you lost_ me ba - by.
F#m7
C#m7
4fr
G#m7
4fr
F#m7
Yea,_ yea,_ ba - by

C#m7
G#m7
F#m7
4fr
- mem - ber when days were like that, I was lov-ing you ev-ery time_ you loved back, and now you're
tell-ing me that_ you miss that, bet you feel lone - ly___ but it's like_ that. Do you re -
1.
2.
- ly___ that you lost__ me I bet you feel lone - ly.

DEEPER UNDERGROUND

Words and Music by JASON KAY,
TOBY SMITH, STUART ZENDER,
DERRICK MCKENZIE, SIMON KATZ
and WALLIS BUCHANAN

D5 5fr
F#5 E5 C#5 4fr
wreck it down yeah.
D5 5fr
F#5 E5 C#5 4fr
Some-thing's come to rock_ me and I can't keep my head, I get ner-vous in the
pock - et full of mon - ey and an eye full of hate, take a plea-sure in de -
D5 5fr
F#5 E5 C#5 4fr
New York ci - ty streets,_ where my le - ga - cy treads, I know I'm bet-ter off
-struc-tion of the ve - ry thing___ that they tried to cre - ate, some-bo - dy tell me why does
D5 5fr
F#5 E5 C#5 4fr
stand - ing in the sha - dows, far from hu - mans with guns,__ but now
all man - kind,___ on - ly tam - per and touch, have a ha - bit where they

D5
5fr
F#5
E5
C#5
4fr
it's too late, there's no es-cape from what they have done. Come on.
bite off more than they can chew and now it's too much.
C#m
4fr
Am/C
Am
I'm go - ing deep - er un - der - ground,
E
D/A
C#m/G#
4fr
C#m
4fr
there's too much pa - nic in this town. I'm go - ing deep - er un - der - ground,
Am/C
Am
E
D/A
C#m/G#
4fr
there's too much pa - nic in this town.

C#m
Am/C
Am
to Coda
— I'm go - ing deep - er un - der - ground, _ and I've got __ to go
E
D/A
C#m/G#
1.
C#5
D5
deep - er ___ deep - er, deep - er, deep - er yeah.
F#5
E5
C#5
D5
They're gon - na wreck it down now
F#5
E5
C#5
D5
(scat)

F♯5
E5
C♯5
4fr
D5
5fr
Hey yeah we're gon - na bring it down yeah
F♯5
E5
C♯5
4fr
Some peo - ple with a
2.
C♯m
4fr
C♯/E♯
E7
B♭
C♯
4fr
E♯m
E
B♭

C♯5 4fr
D5 5fr
F♯5 E5 C♯5 4fr
I'm go - ing, I'm go - ing, I'm go - ing deep - er un - der - ground,
D5 5fr
F♯5 E5 C♯5 4fr
D.𝄋 al Coda
I'm go - ing, I'm go - ing, I'm go - ing deep - er un - der - ground,
⊕ CODA
E
D/A
C♯m/G♯ 4fr
C♯m 4fr
there's too much pa - nic in this town. I'm go - ing deep - er un - der - ground.
repeat to fade
Am/C
Am
E
D/A
C♯m/G♯ 4fr

FLYING WITHOUT WINGS

Words and Music by
STEVE MAC and WAYNE HECTOR

Fm7(add11)
D♭
- er's eyes.
your life.
Who can de - ny the joy it brings when you've found that spe-cial
And when you know how much that means, you've found that spe-cial
E♭
A♭add9
1.
thing. You're fly - ing with-out wings.
thing. You're fly - ing with-out wings.
(2.) Some find it shar - ing ev - 'ry
2.
A♭
E♭/G
D♭add9
E♭
So im-pos - si - ble as they may seem, you've got to
Fm7
E♭/G
A♭
E♭/G
D♭add9
fight for e - ve - ry dream. Cos who's to know which one you let

D♭m
E♭11
E♭
E♭11
E♭
go will have made you com - plete. With me it's waking up be -
A♭
D♭/A♭
A♭
E♭/G
Fm7
D♭/F
- side you, to watch the sun rise on your face,
Fm7
D♭
E♭/D♭
D♭
to know that I can say I love you, at an - y giv - en time or
E♭
A♭/E♭
E♭7
A♭
D♭/A♭
place. It's lit-tle things that on - ly I know,

A♭
E♭/G
Fm7
D♭/F
Fm7
those are the things that make you mine.
And it's like fly - ing with-out
D♭
E♭
A♭
wings, 'cause you're my spe-cial thing. I'm fly-ing with-out wings.
D♭
E♭
And you're the place my life be-gins and you'll be where it ends, I'm fly-ing with-out
D♭
Dm7(♭5)
E♭11
rit.
A♭
wings, and that's the joy you bring. I'm fly-ing with-out wings.

IF YOU HAD MY LOVE

Words and Music by RODNEY JERKINS,
LASHAWN DANIELS, FRED JERKINS,
COREY ROONEY and JENNIFER LOPEZ

Bm
you had my love and I gave you all my trust would you com-
Em7
F♯m7
-fort me? { Tell me, ba-by. } And if
Bm
some-how you knew that your love would be un-true would you lie
Em7
F♯m7
to me and call me ba-by?
{ Now if I give you
You said you want my

Bm
me, this is how it s got to be: First of all, I
love and you ve got to have it all. But, first there are some
Em7
F♯m7
won t take you cheat - ing on me. Tell me who can I
things you need to know. If you wan - na
Bm
trust if I can t trust in you? And I re - fuse to
live with all I have to give I need to feel true
Em7
F♯m7
let you play me for a fool. You said,
love or it s got to end, yeah. I don t

Bm
that we could pos - si - bly spend e - ter -
want you tryin to get with me and I end up un -
Em7
F#m7
But if you
So be - fore
- ni - ty. See, thats what you told me, thats what you said.
- hap - py. I dont need the hurt and I dont need the pain.
Bm
want me you have to be ful - fill - ing all
I do give my - self to you, Ill have to know
1
Em7
F#m7
my dreams. If you real - ly want me, babe. If

2
Em7
F♯m7
the truth if I spend my life with you. If
Bm
you had my love and I gave you all my trust would you com - fort me?
(What would you do, babe? Tell me right now.) And if
somehow you knew that your love would be un - true would you lie

Em7
1
F♯m7
to me and call me ba - by? If
2
F♯m7
Bm
ba - by?
Don't you lie to me, ba - by.
Mm.
Em7
F♯m7
Yeah.
Ooh no no no.
Ooh.
Bm
Em7

F♯m7
Bm
If ___ you had my love and I gave ___
Em7
F♯m7
___ you all my trust would you com - fort ___ me? Tell me ba - by. ___ And if ___
Bm
Em7
___ some - how you know that your love ___ would be un - true would you lie ___ to ___ me and call me ___
Repeat and Fade
F♯m7
___ ba - by? If ___
Optional Ending
F♯m7
Bm
___ ba - by?

FROZEN

Words and Music by MADONNA CICCONE
and PATRICK LEONARD

Verses 1 & 2:
Fm
1. You on - ly see what your eyes want to see.
2. Now, there's no point in plac - ing the blame,
Eb/F
Db
How can life be what you want it to be? You're fro - zen
and How should know I suf - fer the same. If I should lose you,
Eb
Fm
Eb/F
when your heart's not o - pen.
my heart will be bro - ken.
Verse 3:
Fm
You're so con - sumed with how much you get.
Love is a bird, she needs to fly.
3. You on - ly see what your eyes want to see.

E♭/F
D♭
You waste your time with hate and re - gret. You're bro - ken
Let all the hurt in - side of you die. You're fro - zen
How can life be what you want it to be? You're fro - zen
E♭
Fm
E♭/F
Fm
when your heart's not o - pen.
when your heart's not o - pen.
when your heart's not o - pen.
Chorus:
Fm
B♭m
D♭
A♭
Mm, if I could melt your heart,
Fm
B♭m
G♭
A♭sus
mm, we'd nev - er be a - part.

Fm
B♭m
D♭
A♭
Mm,
give your-self to me.
Fm
B♭m
G♭
A♭sus
To Coda
Mm,
you hold
Fm
1.
the key.
2.
N.C.

1.
2.
D.S. al Coda
Coda
Fm
B♭m
D♭
A♭
the key.
If I could melt your heart.
Fm
B♭m
G♭
A♭
Fm
B♭m
G♭
A♭
Fm

HOW DO I LIVE

Words and Music by DIANE WARREN

F♯m7
G♯m7
C♯m7
Em7/A
ba - by, you would take a - way ev - 'ry - thing good in my life.
And tell me
𝄋 Chorus:
D
A
G
F♯m7
D
A
now, how do I live with - out you? I want to know.
How do I breathe with - out
G
F♯m7
Bm7
Em7
F♯m7
G(9)
you, if you ev - er go?
How do I ev - er,
ev - er sur - vive?
To Coda
1.
Em7/A
D
F♯m7/B
How do I, how do I, oh, how do I live?
2. With - out you.
2.
Em7/A
D
F♯m
Em7
how do I, oh, how do I live?

Bm7
F♯m7
F♯m7/B
If
G♯m7
C♯m7
F♯m7
you ev - er leave,
ba - by, you would take a - way ev - 'ry - thing.
G♯m7
C♯m7
F♯m7
Need you with me.
Ba - by, 'coz you know that you're ev - 'ry - thing
G♯m7
C♯m7
Em7/A
D.S. 𝄋 al Coda
good in my life.
And tell me

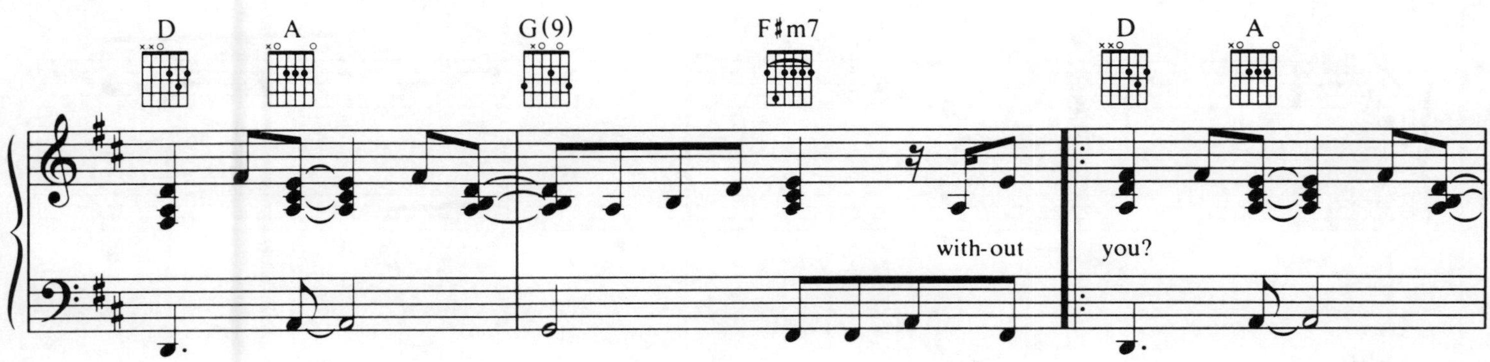

Repeat ad lib. and fade
(vocal 1st time only)

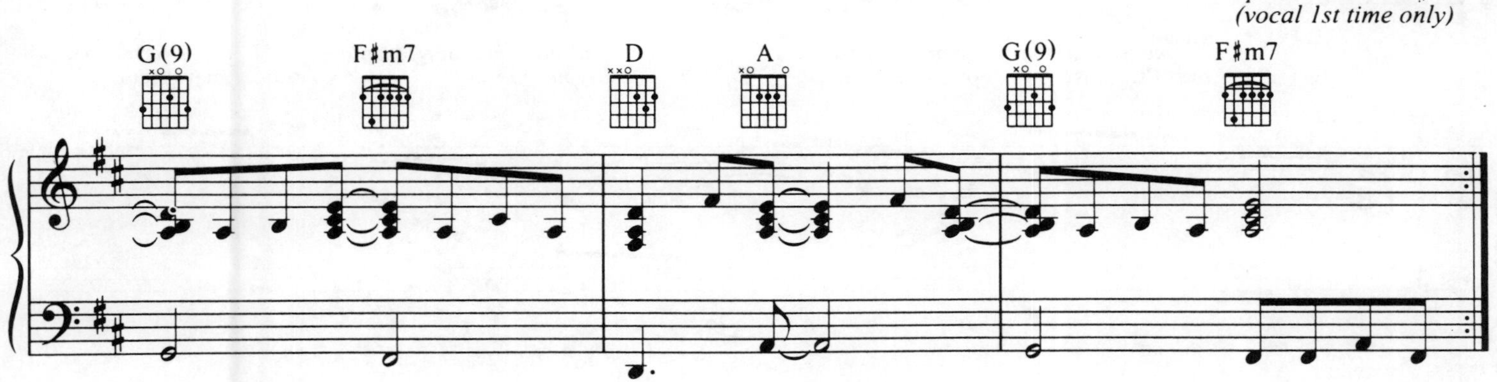

Verse 2:
Without you, there'd be no sun in my sky,
There would be no love in my life,
There'd be no world left for me.
And I, baby, I don't know what I would do,
I'd be lost if I lost you.
If you ever leave,
Baby, you would take away everything real in my life.
And tell me now...
(To Chorus:)

I TRY

Words and Music by MACY GRAY,
DAVE WILDER, JINSOO LIM
and JEREMY RUZUMNA

Em7
G
-geth-er babe, but we're— not. I play it off, but I'm dream-
just a front, just a— front. Hey! I play it off, but I'm dream-
F♯m7
Em7
A
-ing of you.— And I'll keep my cool— but I'm fiend - ing.—
-ing of you.— And I'll keep my cool— but I'm fiend - ing.—
I try to say good-
D
A
-bye and I choke, I try to walk a - way and I stum - ble. Though I try to
Em7
G
A7sus4
D
hide it, it's clear,— my world crum-bles when you are not here. Good-bye and I choke, I try to walk a-

A
Em7
1.
G
A7sus4
- way and I stum - ble. Though I try to hide it, it's clear, my world crum - bles when you are not here.
2.
G
A7sus4
Fmaj7
Am7
crum - bles when you are not here. Here is my con - fes - sion. May I be your pos -
Fmaj7
Em7
C9
- ses - sion? Boy, I need your touch, your love, kiss - es and such. With all my might I try,
Bm7
Em7
but this I can't de - ny, de - ny.

G
F♯m7
Em7
I play it off but I'm dream - ing of you.
And I'll keep my cool, but I'm
A
B♭
E♭
B♭
fiend-ing. I try to say good - bye and I choke, I try to walk a-way and I stum-ble. Though I try to
Fm7
A♭
B♭7sus4
E♭
hide it, it's clear, my world crum-bles when you are not here. Good - bye and I choke, I try to walk a-
Repeat ad lib. to fade
B♭
Fm7
A♭
B♭7sus4
-way and I stum-ble. Though I try to hide it, it's clear, my world crum-bles when you are not here. Good -

FROM THE HEART

Words and Music by DIANE WARREN

Em7
A/C#
Cmaj7
— that's deep_ and true,___ ten-der and strong___ e-nough for you,_
— through ev - ery storm,___ I'll keep you safe,___ I'll keep_ you warm,
B/D#
4fr
E7
Asus4 2
— you can't trust___ this love,_ hon-est that's the hon-est truth.___
— and you'll have___ no doubt_ you're the one I'm liv-ing for.___
Asus2
G
A/C#
— From the heart___ I'm giv - ing you ev -
Bm7
A/C#
D
G
- ery-thing, ev - ery-thing._ From_ the heart

A/C# Bm7
I pro-mise you that I'll be there, I'll be there to love you.
G A/C# Bm7
From the soul I'm show - ing you all I feel, all
A/C# D G A/C# Asus4
I feel is from the heart, from the heart.
1. Bm7 Asus4 2 Dsus4 D
2. Bm7 Asus4 Gmaj7
I'll pro - vide the love

F#7 Bm7 E7

— you need, — just touch — my touch, be - lieve — in me. — I'll ne -

Cmaj7 B Em

- ver make — you cry, — give it all — I've got — with

A11 3fr Gadd9 A/C#

all I've got is all from — the heart, — I'm giv - ing you ev -

Bm7 A/C# D G

- ery - thing, ev - ery - thing. — From — the heart,

A/C#
Bm7
I pro-mise you that I'll be there, I'll be there to love you.
G
A/C#
Bm7
From the soul I'm show - ing you all I feel, all
A/C#
D
G
A/C#
Bm7
Asus2
A
I feel is from the heart, from the heart. mm mm
G
A
D
Dsus4
D
From the heart, from the heart.

IN OUR LIFETIME

Words and Music by JOHN MCELHONE
and SHARLEEN SPITERI

A
I'm not na - ked,
and the min - utes,
you look at me and who I
yeah time has such a puz-zling
G#m
4fr
am.
grace.
Un-der - stand that it is hard to tell you that
A
I've gi - ven all I have to give.
G#m
4fr
And I can un - der-stand your feel - ings, but then ev -

A
B
- ery-bo - dy has_ a life to live._____ Once in a
E
Eadd9
E
Eadd9
Amaj7
A6
life - time, you have seen what I've seen, you will al - ways swim_ for shore.
Amaj7
A6
F#m7
F#m9
F#m
Amaj7
A6
Once in my life - time,___ I'll ne - ver be in - be - tween,
1.
2.
B6
B
B6
B
B6
B
some things you just can't_ ig - nore._____ Once in a

E
Eadd9
E
Eadd9
Amaj7
A6
life-time,
you have seen what I've seen,
you will al-ways swim_ for shore.
Amaj7
A6
F#m7
F#m9
F#m
Amaj7
A6
Once in my life - time,
I'll ne-ver be in - bet-ween,
B6
B
B6
B
E6
E
E6
some things you just can't_ ig - nore.
I just need to have your love, I just
E6
E
E6
Eadd9
A
Asus2
A
A
Asus2
A
can't say no.
It's a gift from way_ a - bove,
I just can't say no.
It's the one

Badd9
B
Badd9
Badd9
B
Bsus4 2
E6
E
E6
big dif-ference. If there's one thing I can't have, I just can't say no, I just can't say
E
Eadd9
E
Eadd9
E
Eadd9
no. (Hey, hey, hey) Once in a life-time, you have seen what I've seen,
Amaj7
A6
Amaj7
A6
F#m7
F#m9
F#m
you will al-ways swim for shore. Once in my life - time,
repeat to fade
Amaj7
A6
B6
B
B6
B
I'll ne-ver be in - be-tween, some things you just can't ig - nore. Once in a

KISS ME

Words and Music by MATT SLOCUM

E♭
E♭maj7
— swing, — swing, swing the spin-ning step,
— bring, — bring, bring your flower-ed hat,
E♭7
A♭
you wear those shoes and I will — wear that dress, oh, —
we'll take the trail marked on your fa - ther's map, oh, —
Fm7
B♭
E♭
Cm
kiss — me —
be - neath the milk - y twi - light,
Fm7
B♭
E♭
E♭7
Fm7
B♭
lead — me —
out on the moon - lit floor, —
lift your o-pen hand

Eb
Bb/D
Cm7
Eb
strike up the band_ and make_ the fire - flies dance, sil - ver moon's spark -
to Coda ⊕
1.
Abmaj7
Bbsus4
Bb
Eb
Ebmaj7
- ling.
So kiss me.
Eb7
Ebmaj7
2.
Eb
Ebmaj7
Eb7
me.
Ebmaj7
Fm7
Bb
Eb
Cm
Fm7
Bb

D.𝄋 al Coda

𝄌 *CODA*

Eb Eb7 Eb Ebmaj7

me.

Eb7

1. Ebmaj7

So kiss

2. Ebmaj7

So kiss

Eb Ebmaj7 Eb7

me.

1. Ebmaj7

So kiss

2. Ebmaj7

Eb

LET ME ENTERTAIN YOU

Words and Music by ROBBIE WILLIAMS
and GUY CHAMBERS

F
Ab
Bb
F
let me entertain you,
F
Ab
Bb
F
let me entertain you.
F
Ab/F
3fr
Look me up in the yel-low pa - ges, I will be your rock of a - ges, your
Bb/F
F
see through fads and your cra - zy pha-ses, yeah.
Lit-tle Bo Peep has lost his sheep, he

A♭/F
3fr
B♭/F
F
3
popped a pill and fell a-sleep, the dew is wet but the grass is sweet my dear.
A♭/E♭
B♭/D
Your mind gets burned with the ha - bits you've learned, but we're the ge - ne - ra - tion that's
He may be good he may be out - ta sight but he can't be here so come a -
F
A♭/E♭
got to be heard, you're tired of your tea-chers and your school's a drag,_ you're
- round to-night here is the place where the feel - ing grows, you
B♭/D
F
to Coda ⊕
F
not going to end_ up like your mum and dad._ So come on let me
got - ta get high_ be-fore you taste the lows._ So come on

A♭
B♭
1.2.
F
3.
F
D.𝄋 al Coda
— en - ter-tain — you,
CODA
F
A♭/F
3fr
B♭/F
1.
F
2.
F
F
A♭
Let me — en - ter-tain
B♭
F
play 4 times
F
— you.
Come on, come on, come on, come on, —

Bbsus4/Eb
Bb/D
F
come on, come on, come on, come on,
come on, come on, come on, come on.
F
Ab
Bb
F
Ab
Bb
F
F
Ab
Bb
F
play 3 times and fade
Let me en-ter-tain you,
lèt me en-ter-tain you.

IT'S NOT RIGHT BUT IT'S OKAY

Words and Music by RODNEY JERKINS,
LASHAWN DANIELS, FRED JERKINS,
ISAAC PHILLIPS and TONI ESTES

Fm
3fr
Cm
3fr
If six of you went out, uh, then
four of you were real - ly cheap, yeah. 'Cause on - ly
Fm
3fr
Cm
3fr
two of you had din - ner: I found your cre - dit card re - ceipt. It's not
Fm7
3fr
Cm
3fr
right, but it's o - kay, I'm gon-na make it a - ny - way. Pack your

Fm7
3fr
Cm
3fr
bag, up and leave, don't you dare come run-ning back to
Fm7
3fr
me. It's not right, but it's o - kay, I'm gon-na
Cm
3fr
Fm7
3fr
make it a - ny - way. Close the door be - hind you, leave your
Cm
3fr
key, I'd ra-ther be a - lone than un - hap - py.

Fm
3fr
I'll pack a bag so you can leave town for a
Cm
3fr
week, yes I am.
Fm
3fr
The phone
ring,
Cm
3fr
and then you look at me.
Fm
3fr
Why turn and look at me? You

Cm
3fr
said it was one of your friends, down on Fif - ty -
Fm
3fr
- fourth Street, boy. So why did two or three
Cm
3fr
show up on your cal - ler I. D., oh?
Fm7
3fr
Cm7
3fr
I've been through all this be - fore, don't

Fm7
3fr
think a - bout it, don't think a - bout it.
Get going, get going, heh,
Cm7
3fr
G♭maj7
Fm7
3fr
things are gon - na change, ba - by.
You don't
Cm7
3fr
stand no chance, boy,
I say yeah, yeah, yeah, yeah, yeah, yeah.
Fm7
3fr
Cm7
3fr
Don't you turn a - round,
there's no more tears left

Fm7
3fr
here for you to see. Was it real - ly worth you go - ing out like
Cm
3fr
that, tell me, oh?
Fm7
3fr
See I'm
mov - ing on,
Cm
3fr
and I re - fuse to turn
back, yeah.
Fm7
3fr
See, all of this time

Cm
3fr
I thought I had some - bo - dy down for Whit - ney.
Fm7
3fr
It turns out
Cm
3fr
you were mak - ing a fool of me, oh. It's not
Fm7
3fr
Lead vocals ad lib.
right, but it's o - kay, I'm gon - na make it a - ny -
Cm
3fr

Fm7
3fr
- way. Pack your bag, up and leave, don't you
Cm
3fr
Fm7
3fr
dare come run-ning back to me. It's not right, but it's o -
Cm
3fr
Fm7
3fr
- kay, I'm gon-na make it a - ny - way. Close the door be - hind you, leave your
Cm
3fr
repeat to fade
key, I'd ra-ther be a - lone than un - hap - py. It's not

LOVE'S GOT A HOLD OF MY HEART

Words and Music by ANDREW FRAMPTON
and PETER WATERMAN

E♭m6/G♭
B♭/F
F
B♭/A♭
E♭/G
please an' save me. There's no doubt, ba-
for-ev-er. An' no mis-take, it's tra-
(D.𝄋. instrumental)
B♭/F
F
Fm
-by you took me pris-'ner, I con-fess, when you
-gic but I have to face the truth I guess, an'
G7
E♭m6/G♭
crossed my de-fen-ces and cap-tured my heart. An' now it's too late
live ev-er-more re-signed to my fate. 'Cos now it's too late
B♭
B♭aug
E♭
E♭m6
to put up a fight. I thought I was strong, but as hard as I try…
to put up a fight. I thought I was strong, but try as I might
can't break a-way.

B♭/F
B♭aug/F♯
E♭
F7sus4
To Coda
Darl - in' there's no way out. No - thing can help me now. Love's got a hold on my
1.
B♭
E♭/B♭
F7sus4/B♭
heart. (My heart, my heart.) (Love's got a hold on my
2. There's
2.
B♭/F
B♭aug/F♯
E♭
F7sus4
heart. Yeah, yeah. Your love's got a hold on my
B♭
B♭/A♭
G7sus4
G7/B
E♭m6/C
E♭m6/G♭
heart. Hold on my heart. Hold on my

B♭
F7sus4
F7
D.%. al Coda
heart.
(Love's got a hold on my, it's got a hold on my heart.)
Coda
B♭
B♭aug
E♭
E♭m6
heart.
Can't break a - way.
B♭/F
B♭aug/F♯
E♭
F7sus4
Darl - in' there's no way out. No - thing can help me now. Love's got a hold on my
B♭/F
B♭aug/F♯
E♭
F7sus4
B♭
heart. Oh, oh. Your love's got a hold on my heart.

MY HEART WILL GO ON

Words by WILL JENNINGS
Music by JAMES HORNER

B/F♯
A
know you go on.
E
B/F♯
A/E
Far a - cross the dis - tance and spac - es be -
E
B
E
B/F♯
tween us you have come to show you go
A
G♯m
C♯m
on.
Near,
mf
mf

B
A
B
far, wher - ev - er you are, I be -
C#m
4fr
B
A
lieve that the heart does go on.
G#m
4fr
F#m
C#m
4fr
B
Once more, you
A
B
C#m
4fr
o - pen the door and you're here in my

B
A
B
heart, and my heart will go on and
E
B/F♯
on. Love can touch us one time and
p
mp
mp
A/E
E
B
E
last for a life - time, and nev - er
B/F♯
A
let go till we're gone.

E
B/F♯
A/E
Love was when I loved you, one true time I
E
B
E
B/F♯
hold to. In my life we'll al - ways go
A
G♯m
C♯m
4 fr
4 fr
on. Near,
mf
mf
B
A
B
far, wher - ev - er you are, I be -

C♯m
B
A
lieve that the heart does go on.
G♯m
F♯m
C♯m
B
Once more, you
A
B
C♯m
o - pen the door and you're here in my
B
A
B
heart, and my heart will go on and

C#m
4fr
B
A
on.
B
C#m
4fr
B
A
G#5
4fr
F#5
Slightly slower
Fm
You're
f
rall.
f
E♭
3fr
D♭
E♭
3fr
here, there's noth - ing I fear, and I

Fm
Eb
3 fr
Db
know that my heart will go on.
Cm
Bbm
Fm
Eb
We'll stay for - ev -
er this way. You are safe in my
heart, and my heart will go on and

Fm
Eb
3 fr
Db
on.
mf
mp

A♭
4 fr
E♭/B♭
6 fr
D♭/A♭
4 fr
A♭maj7
Oh.
pp
mp
p
A♭
4 fr
E♭/B♭
6 fr
D♭/A♭
4 fr
Oh.
pp
pp
A♭
4 fr
p
rit.
p

LIVIN' LA VIDA LOCA

Words and Music by
ROBI ROSA and DESMOND CHILD

C♯m
fr4
2. She's in - to new sen - sa - tions, new kicks in the can-dle - light.
(Verse 3 see block lyric)
She's got a new ad - dic - tion s'full ev - 'ry day and night. She'll
F♯m
G♯m
fr4
make you take your clothes off and go dan - cing in the rain. She'll make

A
B
you live her cra - zy life or she'll take a - way your pain like a bul-
[G♯]
C♯m
- let to your brain.
Up - side in - side out, she's
B add9
C♯m
liv - in' la vi - da lo - ca.
She'll push and pull you down,
B add9
C♯m
liv - in' la vi - da lo - ca.
Her lips are de - vil red and her

Badd9
fr7
C♯m
fr4
skin's the col - our of moc - ca.
She will— wear— you out,—
liv-in' la vi - da lo - ca.
Liv-in' la vi - da lo - ca,
she's
liv-in' la vi - da lo - ca.
1.

2.
F♯m
She'll make you take your clothes off and go dan-
G♯m
fr4
A
-cing in the rain. She'll make you live her cra-zy life or she'll take
B
[G♯]
a-way your pain like a bul-let to your brain.

C♯m
Badd9
C♯m
Up - side, in - side out, she's liv-in' la vi - da lo - ca. She'll
Badd9
C♯m
push and pull you down, liv-in' la vi - da lo - ca. Her
Badd9
C♯m
lips are de - vil red and her skin's the col - our of moc - ca.
Badd9
C♯m
She will wear you out, liv-in' la vi - da lo - ca.

Verse 3:
Woke up in New York City
In a funky cheap hotel
She took my heart and she took my money
She must have slipped me a sleepin' pill
She never drinks the water
Makes you order French champagne
And once you've had a taste of her
You'll never be the same
Yeah, she'll make you go insane.

Upside, inside out *etc.*

A LITTLE BIT OF LOVIN'

Words and Music by GORDON CHAMBERS, ROBBIE NEVIL and BRADLEY SPALTER

D7
G/D
Gm6/D
3fr
am sit-ting here wait - ing an - ti - ci - pat - ing when to make my
are off in your own world but ev - ery guy's girl has got their eyes on
D
D7
G/D
move. I'm so con - fused don't wan - na be ag - gres-sive but my con -
you. And I don't know who you've been kiss - in', may - be you've been
Gm6/D
3fr
D
- fes - sion is that I'm think - in' 'bout you.
miss - in' the kind of love that's true.
Bm
G7
Bm
You might think that a girl like me won't ap-proach you more qui -

E7
Bb7
Aaug
N.C.
- et - ly, but to - night I'm gon - na make you see. When you
D7
G/D
need, (ah) a lit - tle bit of lov - in' ba - by look no
Gm6/D
3fr
D
D7
fur - ther, just think a - bout me. And when you need (need) a lit - tle bit of
G/D
Gm6/D
3fr
to Coda
1.
D
fire all I de - sire is that you think a - bout me. There you

2.
D
Gm7
3fr
me, a - bout me, a - bout me. I don't know when or where
C7/G
Dsus4 2
but this time I don't care, 'cos I got feel - ings to share
and boy you bet - ter be - ware.
This time I'm mak - ing my move,
C7/B♭
A7sus4
D.𝄋 al Coda
N.C.
some-one's got to pur - sue, to-night my vic - tim is you.
Ooh, when you

CODA
D
D7
me. (You got to think a-bout me.) When you need a lit-tle bit of
G/D
Gm6/D
3fr
lov - in' ba - by look no fur - ther, just think a - bout
D
D7
G/D
me. And when you need a lit-tle bit of lov - in' all I de -
Gm6/D
3fr
D
repeat ad lib. to fade
- sire is that you think a - bout me. When you

MUSIC TO WATCH GIRLS BY

Words by TONY VERONA
Music by SID RAMIN

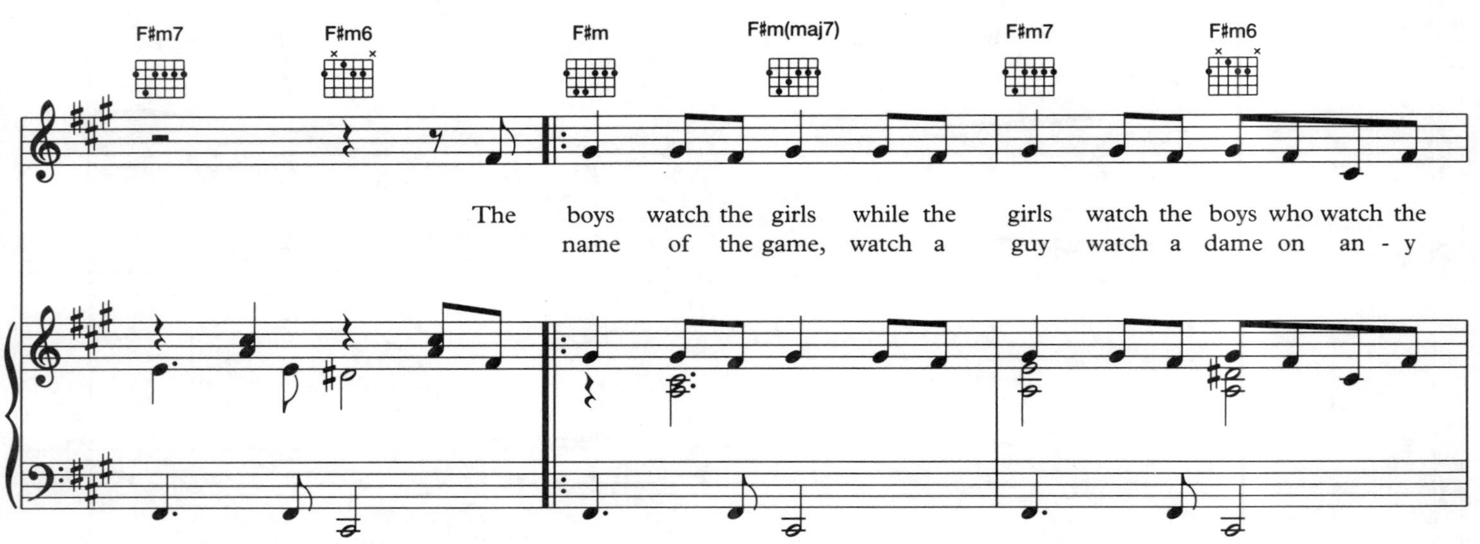

1.
2.
G#7
4fr
C#7
F#7
-vene to make the scene. Which is the Guys talk,
-cross, ro-mance is boss.
Bm
E7
A
C#7
girls talk it hap-pens ev-ery-where. Eyes watch,
F#m
G#7
C#7
girls walk with ten-der lov-ing care. It's keep-ing
F#m
F#m(maj7)
F#m7
F#m6
G#7
track of the pack watch-ing them watch-ing back that makes the world go round.

Bm
G#7
4fr
Watch that sound each time you hear a loud col - lec-tive sigh
C#7
F#m
Bm
F#m
C#
4fr
D
they're mak-ing mus - ic to watch girls by.
Gm
3fr
Gm(maj7)
3fr
Gm7
3fr
Gm6
A7
Cm
3fr
A7
1.
D7

2.
G7
Cm
3fr
F7
Guys talk, girls talk it hap-pens ev-ery - where.
B♭
D7
Gm
3fr
A7
D7
— Eyes watch, girls walk with ten-der lov-ing care.
Gm
3fr
Gm(maj7)
3fr
Gm7
3fr
Gm6
— It's keep-ing track of the pack watch-ing them watch-ing back that makes the
A7
Cm
3fr
world go round. Watch that sound each time you hear a

A7
D7
Gm
3fr
Cm
3fr
Gm
3fr
loud col - lec - tive sigh they're mak - ing mus - ic to watch girls by.
Gm
3fr
Gm(maj7)
3fr
The boys watch the girls while the
la la la la la la
Gm7
3fr
Gm6
A7
Cm
3fr
girls watch the boys who watch the girls go by, eye to eye,
la la la la la la la la la la la la la
A7
D7
Fade
they sol - emn - ly con - vene to make the scene. La la la
la la la la la la la la la la

NEW YORK CITY BOY

Words and Music by NEIL TENNANT,
CHRISTOPHER LOWE and DAVID MORALES

B♭maj7
Gm6
Am7
New York Ci - ty boy, you'll ne - ver have a bored
Dm
B♭maj7
Gm6
day, 'cause you're a New York Ci - ty boy where Sev - enth
Am7
Dm
B♭maj7
A - ve - nue meets Broad - way.
1. When you're a boy,
2. The street is a - maz - ing, the
Gm6
Am7
Dm
some days are tough, ly - ing on your bed play - ing punk rock and stuff.
hoo - chies un - real, check out all the hard - ware at the lat - est deal.

B♭maj7
Gm6
Am7
Home is a boot camp, you've got to es - cape, want to go and wan - der in the
Hear a song, that's the bomb! If you don't get that mix, it's gone
Dm
B♭maj7
Gm6
tic - ker - tape. You feel the deal is real.
eigh - ty - six. You feel the deal is real.
Am7
Dm
1.
B♭maj7
You're a New York Ci - ty boy. So
You're in New York Ci - ty.
Gm6
Am7
Dm
young, so run in - to New York Ci - ty.

2.
B♭maj7
Gm6
Am7
New York Ci - ty boy, you'll ne - ver have a bored
New York Ci - ty boy, this is your re - ward
Dm
B♭maj7
Gm6
day, 'cause you're a New York Ci - ty boy, where Sev-enth
day, 'cause you're a New York Ci - ty boy, where Sev-enth
Am7
Dm
N.C.
A - ve - nue meets Broad - way.
A - ve - nue meets Broad - way.
Cmaj7
3
And as the eve - ning

F♯m7
Cmaj7
falls,
F♯m7
Cmaj7
3
you can re - turn its
F♯m7
Cmaj7
calls.
F♯m7
Cmaj7
1.
F♯m7
2.
C6

Cmaj7
D11
You feel
the deal
is real.
You're a New York Ci-ty boy.
Bbmaj7
Gm6
Am7
Dm
So young,
so run
in-to New York Ci-ty.

B♭maj7
Gm6
Am7
New York Ci - ty boy, you'll ne - ver have a bored
New York Ci - ty boy, this is your re - ward
Dm
B♭maj7
Gm6
day, 'cause you're a New York Ci - ty boy, where Sev-enth
day, 'cause you're a New York Ci - ty boy, where Sev-enth
Am7
1–7.
Dm
8.
Dm
A - ve - nue meets Broad - way. - way, 'cause you're a
A - ve - nue meets Broad - way.
B♭maj7
N.C.
New York Ci - ty boy, where Sev-enth A - ve - nue meets Broad - way.

MY LOVE IS YOUR LOVE

Words and Music by WYCLEF JEAN
and JERRY DUPLESSIS

Dm
C
G/B
G
and I'm stand - ing on the front line,
I see de - struc - tion and pov - er - ty,
and I'm home - less on the street,
we stay young for each oth - er's eyes.
C
G/B
Am
F
and the Lord asks me what I did with my life, I'll
and I feel like I want to go home, it's
and I'm sleep - ing in Grand Cen - tral Sta - tion, it's
And no mat - ter how old we get, it's
C
G
C
Gm7
3
will say, "I spent it with you." (Clap your hands, y'all, it's al - right.)
o - kay if you're com - ing with me.
o - kay if you're sleep - ing with me.
o - kay as long as I got you, ba - by.

1.3.
C
Gm7
(Clap your hands, y'all, it's al - right.)
2.4.
C
Gm7
(Clap your hands, y'all, it's al - right.)
C
Gm7
(Clap your hands, y'all, it's al - right.)
Chorus:
C
G
Your love is my love and
Am
F
my love is your love.
C
G
It would take an e - ter - ni - ty to break us,
Am
F
and a chain of all the stars could-n't hold us.
C
G
Your love is my love and

Am
F
C
G
my love__ is your love.__
It would take an e - ter - ni - ty to break us,
1.
Am
F
C
Gm7
and a chain of all the stars could-n't hold us.
(Clap your hands, y'all, it's al - right.__)
C
Gm7
C
Gm7
D.S. 𝄋
(Clap your hands, y'all, it's al - right.__)
(Clap your hands, y'all, it's al - right.__)
2.
Bridge:
Am
F
A♭
B♭
and a chain of all the stars could-n't hold us.
If__ I should die this__ ver - y

Cm
Ab
Bb
day, don't cry, 'cause on earth we was-n't meant to stay.
C
Ab
Bb
And no mat-ter what the peo-
Cm
Ab
Bb
ple say, I'll be wait-ing for you at the, the Judg-ment Day.
G7sus
Chorus:
C
G
Your love is my love and

Am
F
C
G
my love is your love.
It would take an e-ter-ni-ty to break us,
1.2.
3.
and a chain of all the stars could-n't hold us.
and a chain of all the stars could-n't hold us.
Repeat ad lib. and fade
Gm7
(Clap your hands, y'all, it's al-right.)
(Clap your hands, y'all, it's al-right.)

NO SCRUBS

Words and Music by KEVIN BRIGGS,
KANDI BURRUSS and TAMEKA COTTLE

C♯m7
G♯m
D♯7
G♯m
Al - ways talk-in' 'bout what he wants_ and just sits on his broke ass. So
C♯m7
G♯m
D♯7
G♯m
no, I don't want your num - ber, no, I don't want to give you mine, and
C♯m7
G♯m
D♯7
G♯m
no, I don't want to meet you no - where, no, I don't want none of your time. And
Chorus:
C♯m7
G♯m
D♯7
G♯m
no, I don't want no scrub. A scrub is a guy that can't get no love from

C♯m7 G♯m D♯7 G♯m
me. Hang-ing out the pas-sen-ger side of his best friend's ride, try-ing to hol-ler at
C♯m7 G♯m D♯7 G♯m
me. I don't want no scrub. A scrub is a guy that can't get no love from
1.
C♯m7 G♯m D♯7 G♯m
me. Hang-in' out the pas-sen-ger side of his best friend's ride, try-ing to hol-ler at
2. But a
2.
Bridge:
D♯7 G♯m
best friend's ride, try-ing to hol-ler at me.
If you don't have a car and you're walk-ing, oh yes,

D♯7(♭9)
G♯m7
son, I'm talk-ing to you. If you live at home wit' your mom-ma, oh yes,
G7
F♯m7
F7
Emaj9
son, I'm talk-in' to you. If you have a short-y but you don't show love, oh
D♯7/G
G♯m7
C♯9
yes, son, I'm talk-ing to you. Wan-na get with me with no mon-ey, oh
C♯m7/F♯
D♯7/G
C♯m7
G♯m
no, I don't want no.
No

D♯7
G♯m
C♯m7
G♯m
scrub.
No
D♯7
G♯m
C♯m7
G♯m
scrub.
No
D♯7
G♯m
C♯m7
G♯m
scrub.
No
Chorus:
D♯7
G♯m
C♯m7
G♯m
scrub.
No, I don't want no scrub. A
me.

Verse 2:
But a scrub is checkin' me,
But his game is kinda weak.
And I know that he can't approach me,
'Cause I'm lookin' like class and he's lookin' like trash.
'Can't get wit' no deadbeat ass. So
No, I don't want your number,
No, I don't want to give you mine,
No, I don't want to meet you nowhere,
No, I don't want none of your time.
And . . .
(To Chorus:)

RAY OF LIGHT

Words and Music by
MADONNA CICCONE, WILLIAM ORBIT,
CHRISTINE LEACH, CLIVE MULDOON
and DAVE CURTIS

"Ray Of Light" contains a musical sample from "Sepheryn" by Clive Muldoon and Dave Curtis

B♭
E♭
She's got her-self a u - ni - verse gone quick-
She's got her-self a lit - tle piece of heav-
ly,
for the call of thun - der
en,
wait-ing for the time when
threat-ens ev - 'ry one.
earth shall be as one.
And I feel
𝄋 Chorus:
like I just got home, and I feel.
3rd time instrumental

B♭
E♭
And I feel,
like I just got home, and I feel.
To Coda
1.
2.

B♭
E♭
Quick-er than a ray
of light,
quick-er than a ray of light.

Verse:
B♭
Cm7
Dm
E♭
3. Zeph-yr in the sky at night, I won - der do my tears of
mourn - ing sink be-neath the sun?
She's got her-self a u - ni - verse gone quick - ly, for the call of
thun - der threat-ens ev - 'ry one. And I feel
D.S. al Coda

Coda
B♭
E♭
Quick-er than a ray of light, then gone
for some-one else shall be there
through the end - less years.
Repeat ad lib. and fade

S CLUB PARTY

Words and Music by TOR ERIK HERMANSEN,
MIKKEL ERIKSEN, HALLGEIR RUSTAN
and HUGH ATKINS

Bm7
E7
Bm7
(1.) Fi-nal-ly Fri-day night, feel-ing kin-da good, look-in' al-right. Got-ta get mov-in', can't be late, got-ta get
E7
Bm7
E7
groov-in', just can't wait. Hey! Get the feel - in', push the ceil - ing.
(Get the feel - in',) (Push the ceil - ing,)
Bm7
E7
Bm
Pla - ya ha - ters 'cause here we go.
(Pla - ya ha - ters) (Get rea - dy ev - 'ry - bo - dy 'cause here we go.)
𝄋
Bm7
E7
G6
A
D
A/C♯
S Club, gon - na show you how.
(There ain't no party like an S Club party.)
(Everybody get down tonight.)

Bm7
E7
G6
A
D
A/C♯
S Club, gon-na take you high.
(There ain't no party like an S Club party.)
(Shake your body from side to side.)
Bm7
E7
Ooh, ooh, put your hands in the air, ooh, ooh, like you just don't care.
Bm7
E7
N.C.
To Coda
Ooh, ooh, there's a par-ty ov-er there, ooh, ooh, there's a par-ty ov-er there.
Bm7
E7
Bm7
(2.) Ti-na's do-in' her dance, Jon's look-in' for ro-mance. Paul's get-tin' down on the floor, while

E7
Bm7
Han-nah's scream-in' out for more.
You wan-na see Brad-ley swing, you wan-na see
D.%. al Coda
E7
Bm7
E7
Bm
Ra-chel do her thing. Then we got Jo, she got the flow, get rea-dy ev-'ry-bo-dy 'cause here we go.
Coda
Bm7
E7
Ooh, ooh, put your hands in the air, ooh, ooh, like you just don't care.
Bm7
E7
Ooh, ooh, there's a par-ty ov-er there, ooh, ooh, there's a par-ty ov-er there.

N.C.
Yeah, the boys make some noise. (Noise!)
Ooh chi-ma-ma show your na - na.
Bm7
E7
G6
A
D
N.C.
S Club, gon-na show you how.
(There ain't no party like an S Club party.)
(Everybody get down tonight.)
gliss
C♯m7
F♯7
A6
B
E
B/D♯
S Club, gon-na show you how.
(There ain't no party like an S Club party.)
(Everybody get down tonight.)
Repeat to fade
C♯m7
F♯7
A6
B
E
B/D♯
S Club gon-na take you high.
(There ain't no party like an S Club party.)
(Shake your body from side to side.)

SUMMERTIME OF OUR LIVES

Words and Music by PETER CUNNAH,
BENJAMIN ADAMS, CHRISTIAN INGEBRIGSTEN,
PAUL MARAZZI and MARK READ

Em7
Am7
Fmaj7
G
Em7
Am7
sun - light. (Sun - light.) Hot sand, hold - ing you hand. You keep me
on me. (On me.) Blue skies, sea in your eyes. Let the
Fmaj7
G
Em7
Am7
jam - min' in the morn - ing 'til the moon - - - light.
groove move my peo - ple all a - round me.
We'll have the
Fmaj7
G
Em7
Am7
Fmaj7
G
Em7
Am7
gliss
time of our lives, in our won - der - world.
Fmaj7
G
Em7
Am7
Fmaj7
G
E7
gliss
Time of our lives. Come on!
There's a boy for ev - 'ry girl. Come on!

Fmaj7
G
Em7
Am7
Sum-mer - time of our lives, our lives.
1.
To Coda
2.
our lives.
Sum-mer - time,
sum-mer - time,
(Come on!)
N.C.
su-gar can - dy cher - ry world.
Sum-mer - time,
sum-mer - time,
(Come on!)

N.C.
Fmaj7
G
there's a boy for ev - 'ry girl. Sum-mer - time, sum-mer - time,
N.C.
Fmaj7
G
N.C.
su-gar can - dy cher - ry world. Sum-mer - time, sum-mer - time.
Guitar
Fmaj7
G
Em7
Am7
Fmaj7
G
Em7
Am7
8vb
Fmaj7
G
Em7
Am7
Fmaj7
G
Em7
Am7
D.%. al Coda
We'll have the
(8vb)

Coda
Em7
Am7
Fmaj7
G
our lives.
Ba-by get rea-dy, get down.
Are you up for it?
Get down with it.
(Come on!)
(Come on!)
(Come on!)
(Come on!)
8vb
1.
2.
N.C.
Ba-by get rea-dy, get down.
Are you up for it?
Get down.
(Come on!)
(Come on!)
gliss
Sum-mer-time of our lives, our lives.
Sum-mer-time of our lives, our lives.
(Come on!)

SHE

Words and Music by CHARLES AZNAVOUR
and HERBERT KRETZMER

Gbm6/Bbb
3fr
Db/Ab
Db/F
to Coda
sings, may be the chill that au - tumn brings, may be a hun - dred dif - ferent
dreams, a smile re - flec - ted in a stream, she may not be what she may
tears, and make them all my sou - ve - nirs, for where she goes I've got to
1.
Gb
Ab7
Db
Gb
Gb/Ab
Ab7
2.
Eb/G
Ab7sus4
things with-in the mea-sure of a day.
seem in - side her
Db
Gb
Gb/Ab
Ab13
Db
shell.
Edim7
Gb
Gb/Bb
Db
Bb/D

Ebm
Gbm6/Bbb
3fr
Db/Ab
Db/F
Eb/G
Ab7sus4
3fr
Ab7
3fr
Db
A
4fr
E
3fr
She ___ who al-ways seems so hap-py in a crowd, whose eyes can be so pri-vate and so
D
C#
C#/E#
proud, no one's al-lowed to see them when they cry.

F#m
B
E
3fr
C#
She may be the love that can-not hope to last, may come to me from sha-dows of the
Eb
Ab/C
D.S. al Coda
past that I'll re-mem - ber till the day I die.
CODA
Eb/G
Ab7
3fr
Gb
be, the mean-ing of my life is she,
Db/F
Ebm7
poco rit.
Db
she, oh, she.

SWEAR IT AGAIN

Words and Music by
STEVE MAC and WAYNE HECTOR

Eadd9 Gadd9 Dadd9

used to know have just giv - en up, they wan-na let it go, but we're still
- ter-nal - ly, and if you see how beau-ti - ful you are to me, you'll know I'm not

Bm F#7/A#

try - ing. So you should know this love we share was
ly - ing. Sure, there'll be times we wan - na say good-bye, but

Bm/A E A E D

ne - ver made to die. I'm glad we're on this one - way street, just you and I,
ev - en if we tried, there are some things in this life won't be de - nied,

D/E
E
A
just you and I. I'm never gonna say good-
won't be de - nied.
F#m7
D
-bye, 'cause I never wanna see you cry. I swore to you my love would re-
Gadd9
D/E
A
-main and I'd swear it all over again and I, I'm never gonna treat you
F#m7
D
bad, 'cause I never wanna see you sad. I swore to share your joy and your

Gadd9
D/E
to Coda
1.
A
E
Dadd9
2fr
pain, and I swear it all ov - er a - gain, all ov - er a - gain. 2. Some peo-ple say,
2.
Bm7
A/C♯
D
The more I know of you is the more I know I love
Bm7
A/C♯
D
you, and the more that I'm sure I want you for ev - er and ev - er more.
Bm7
A/C♯
D
B/D♯
4fr
And the more that you love me, the more that I know,

poco rit.
D.𝄋 al Coda
E
F#m/E
E
D/E
E
3
oh that I'm ne-ver gon-na let you go, got-ta let you know that
no pedal
with pedal

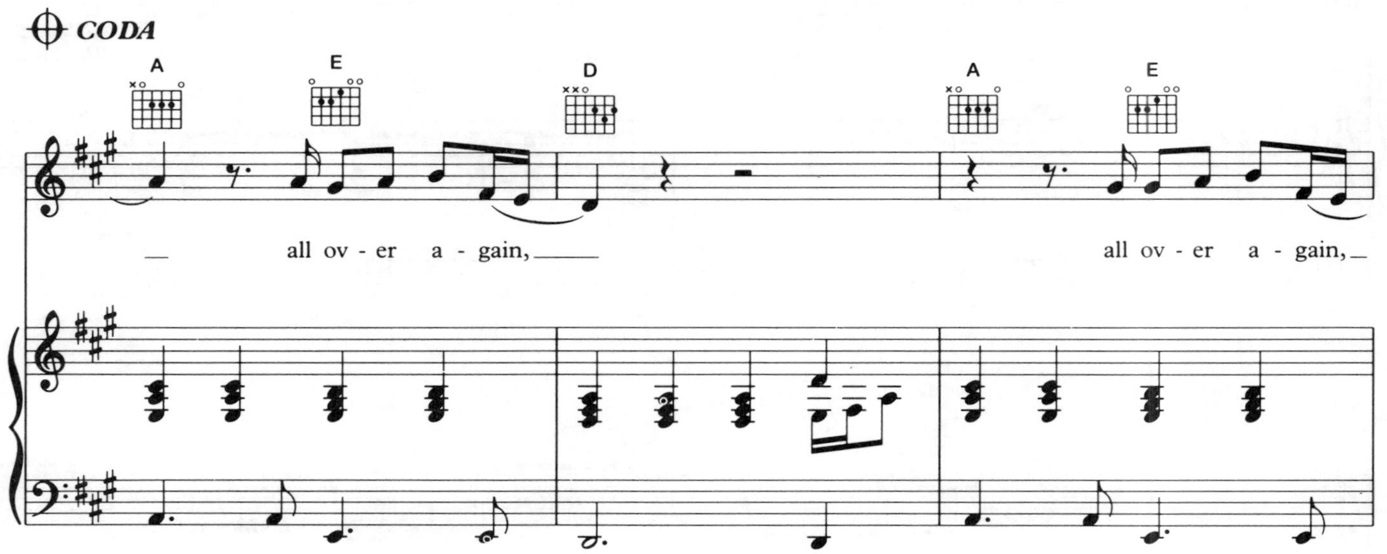
CODA
A
E
D
A
E
all ov - er a - gain,
all ov - er a - gain,

rit.
D
Aadd9
3
and I swear it all ov - er a - gain.

OUTSIDE

Words and Music by GEORGE MICHAEL

C6
Gm9
3fr
C6
I think I'm done with the kit - chen ta - ble, ba -
Gm9
3fr
C6
Gm9
3fr
C6
- by. Let's go out - side_ in the sun - shine,
(let's go out - side) ___
Gm9
3fr
C6
Gm9
3fr
I know you want to, but you can't say yes, (let's go out - side)
let's go out - side
C6
Gm9
3fr
1.
C6
__ in the moon - shine, take me to the pla - ces that I _____ love best. __ So my an -
(2.) in the mean - time,

Gm9
3fr
C6
Gm9
3fr
-gel she says, don't you wor - ry 'bout the things they're say - ing, yeah,
C6
Gm9
3fr
C6
got no friends in high pla - ces and the game that you gave
Gm9
3fr
C6
2.
C6
a - way wasn't worth play - ing. love best. And
Let's go out -
Cm7
3fr
Cm6
Gm9
3fr
yes I've been bad, Doc - tor won't you do with me what you can.

Gm
Cm7
Cm6
3fr
You see I think a-bout it all the time, twen-ty-four
(2.) I'd ser-vice the com-
Gm9
Gm
Cm7
se-ven. You say you want it, you got it, I
-mu-ni-ty (but I al-rea-dy have you see!) I
Cm6
Gm9
Gm
ne-ver real-ly said it be-fore. There's no-thing here
Cm7
Cm6
Dsus4
but flesh and bone, there's no-thing more, no-thing more, there's no-thing more.

Gm9 3fr C6 Gm9 3fr C6

Back to na -

Gm9 3fr C6 Gm9 3fr C6 *to Coda* ⊕

- ture, just hu - man na - ture. Get - ting on back to
Danc - ing on the D - train

Gm9 3fr C6 Gm9 3fr

I think I'm done with the so - fa, I think I'm done with the hall,

C6 Gm9 3fr C6

— I think I'm done with the kit - chen ta - ble, ba -

Gm9
3fr
C6
Gm9
3fr
- by.
Let's go out - side.
(let's go out - side)
C6
Gm9
3fr
C6
in the sun - shine,
I know you want to, but you can't say yes,
(let's go out -
Gm9
3fr
C6
Gm9
3fr
let's go out - side, in the moon - shine,
take me to the pla - ces that I
- side)
C6
N.C.
love best.

G13sus4
D.𝄋 al Coda
CODA
Gm9
3fr
And
ba - by.
C6
Gm9
3fr
C6
When the moon is high
and the grass is jump-
Gm9
3fr
C6
Gm9
3fr
C6
repeat to fade
- in'
come on,
just
keep on
funk - in'

SUNSHINE

Words and Music by
GABRIELLE and JONATHAN SHORTEN

F♯m
Gadd9
Gmaj7
and ful - fil my fan - ta - sies;
and felt that I could fly;
I learnt a lot of tricks to
I'm look-ing at the world in an
F♯m/A
D
Dsus2/C♯
Bm
F♯m/A
help me live my life.
You helped me find my pa - ra - dise,
op - ti - mis - tic light.
You made me ap - pre - ci - ate my life,
Gadd9
G/A
3fr
D
when you came you were like . . .
Sun-shine through my
'cause when you came you were like . . .
Bm7
F♯m
Gadd9
D
win-dow, that's what you are, my shin-ing star.
Mak-ing me feel

1.
2.
Bm7
F#m
Gadd9
Gsus2
A
Bm
D
Cadd9
E
C#m7
G#m
3fr
4fr
I'm on top of the world, telling me I'll go far.
You are the calm when I am the storm, you are the breeze that carries me on.
When I set a drift you anchor at me, you're there for me.
(Sun-shine) Oh yeah, that's what you are, my shin-ing star.

A
E
C#m7
G#m
4fr
Mak-ing me feel
I'm on top of the world,
tell-
ing me that I'll go far.
Sun-shine through my
win-dow,
that's what you are,
my
shin
ing
star.
(Sun-shine)
Mak-ing me feel
I'm on top of the world,
tell
ing me that I'll go far.
repeat ad lib. to fade

SWEET LIKE CHOCOLATE

Words and Music by STEVEN MEADE
and DANIEL LANGSMAN

Dm
C
B♭
(2nd time) Sweet like choco - late.
Dm
C
1.
B♭
You're sweet like
2.
N.C.
N.C.
choco - late, boy.
1. Find - ing a way in the dark ain't so
hard when you're close to my heart. You are there when I'm feel - ing a -

- lone, all I ___ need is for you to come home. You're sweet like
Dm
C
B♭
choco-late, boy, _ sweet like choco - late. You bring me
Dm
C
B♭
so much joy, _ you're sweet like choco - late, _ boy. ______
Dm
C
B♭
2. Trust is the lock, is the key, there's no _ doubt that your love's all for
3. Know - ing you're there ev - ery day, makes me _ high in my own spe - cial

Dm
C
me. You are sweet on the tip of my tongue, you are
way. I am calm in the face of your love, hold - ing
B♭
Dm
warm like the rays of the sun.
you is a gift from a - bove.
You're sweet like choco-late, boy,
C
B♭
Dm
sweet like choco - late.
You bring me so much joy,
C
B♭
you're sweet like choco - late, boy.
You're sweet like . . .

Dm
C
B♭
Da da da da da da da, ba da_ da da da da da da
da. Ba_ da_ da da da da da da da, ba da_
da da da da da da da.
1.
2.
da. Ba_ da_
da da da da da da da, ba da_ da da da da da da da. Ba_ da_
(Sweet like choco - late.)

Dm
C
B♭
da da da da da da da, ba da__ da da da da da da
(You're sweet like choco - late, boy.)
Dm
C
da. Ba__ da__ da da da da da da da, ba da__
(Sweet like
B♭
Dm
da da da da da da da. Ba__ da__ da da da da da da
choco - late.)
C
B♭
repeat to fade
da, ba da__ da da da da da da da. Ba__ da__
(You're sweet like choco - late, boy.)

TO EARTH WITH LOVE

Words and Music by
CLIFF JONES, NICK CROWE,
NIGEL HOYLE and JAMES RISEBERO

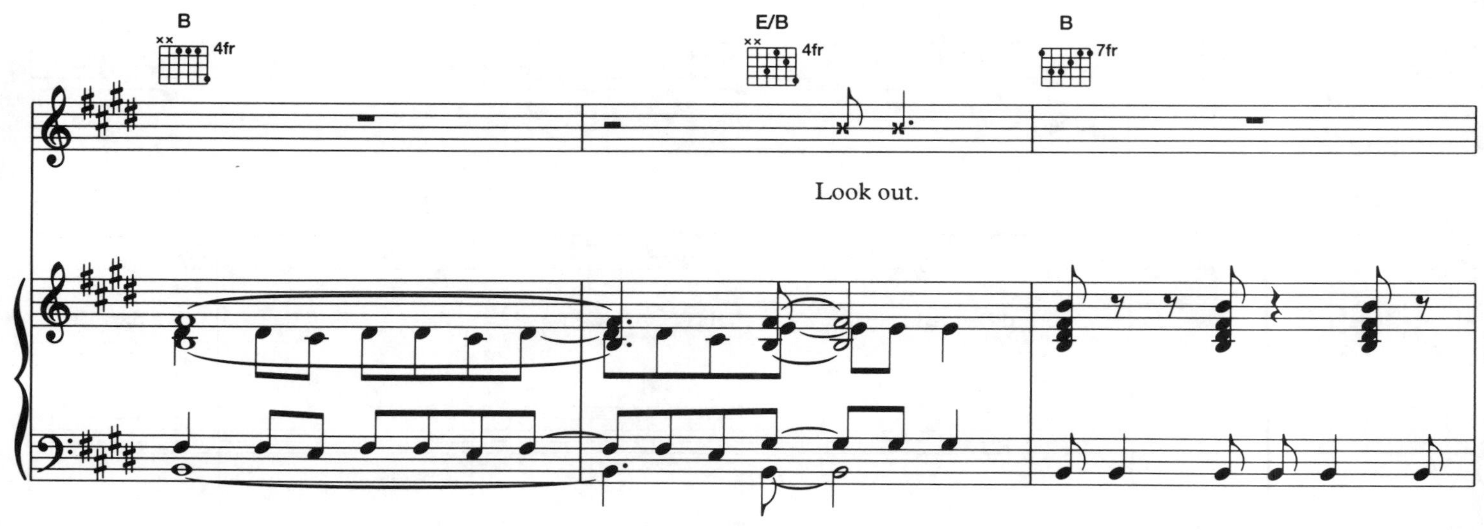

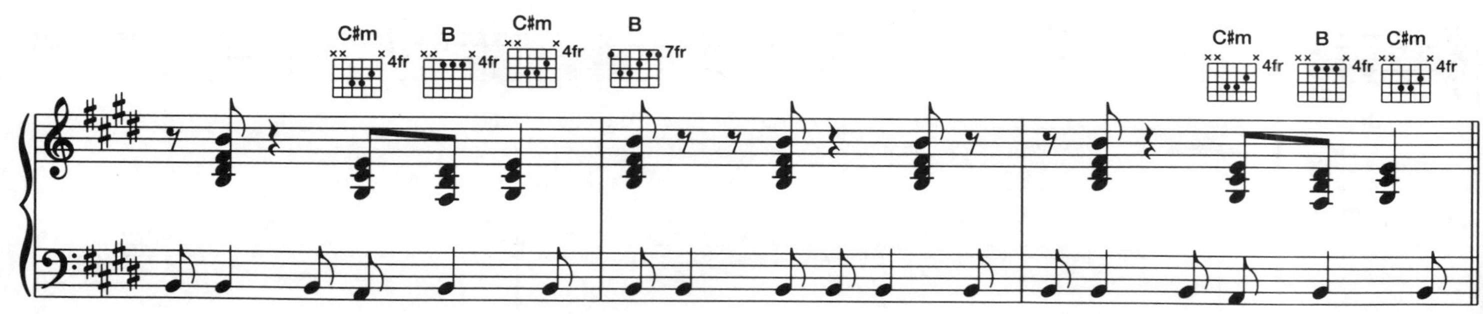

B
C#m
B
C#m
B
7fr
4fr
1. Use the la - test sci - en - ces to make your world a bet -
2. Su - per-na - tural fai - ry tale they told you when you were

C#m
B
C#m
B
- ter place. I - ci - cles and S. R. I.'s
in school. God was good and boys were boys, and

B
C#m
B
C#m
E
Asus2
take the edge and send those blues a - way. It's a beau-ti - ful day
men ne-ver went to the moon. But that's cool. Ae - ro-smith
(3.) let's get it on.
(4.) let's get it on.

E5/B
Aadd9/C#
B
7fr
in my neigh - bour - hood,
rule.
To earth with love,
Put your plat - forms on,
Won't you put the Kraft - werk on.

C#m
B
C#m
B
4fr
7fr
1.
come what may.
from the kids up a - bove.
we can dance 'til dawn.
(Put the Kraft - werk on).

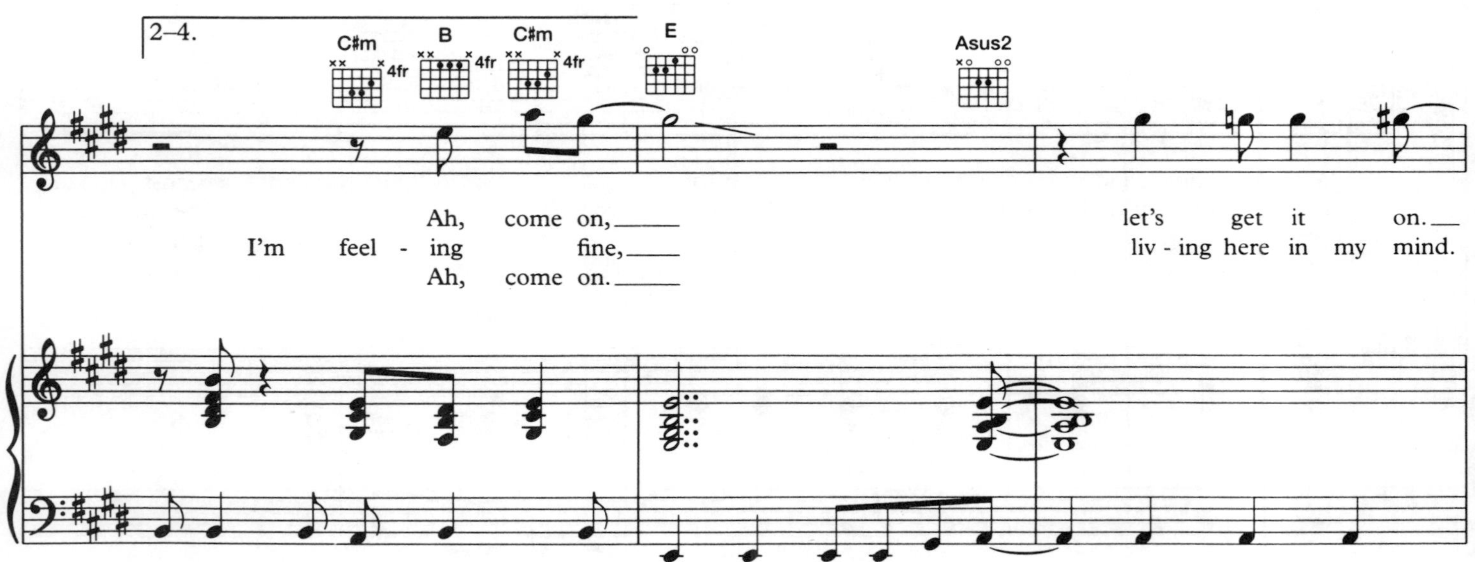
2–4.
C#m
B
C#m
E
Asus2
4fr
Ah, come on,
let's get it on.
I'm feel - ing fine,
liv - ing here in my mind.
Ah, come on.

E5/B
Aadd9/C#
B
7fr
To earth with love,
It's just a mat - ter of time,
To earth with love,
2nd time to Coda
C#m
B
4fr
from the kids up a - bove.
be - fore I feel O. K.
from the kids up a - bove.
F#m7
9fr
Hills I can - not climb,
('cause I have - n't got the time).
E
Things I've ne - ver seen,

B E B E B G#m7
4fr 7fr 11fr 4fr 4fr 4fr
(in a while, in a while, in a while).
G#m7 C#m7 C#7sus4 C#m7 C#7sus4
11fr 9fr 9fr 9fr 9fr
Liv - ing in my head, (in my head, in my head). You bet - ter
A E/G# B Bsus4 B Aadd9/E
5fr 7fr 7fr 7fr 6fr
look out world, 'cause no-thing's gon - na bring me down.
E B C#m B C#m
7fr 4fr 4fr 4fr
1st time only

D.% al Coda x2
B
7fr
1.
C#m
4fr
B
4fr
C#m
4fr
2.
C#m
4fr
B
4fr
C#m
4fr
Look out.
Well come on
CODA
Swing quavers slightly
A
5fr
F#
2fr
Let's ask the fam - ily,
E
Aadd9/E
6fr
is there a - ny - thing left to love?
repeat to fade
E
Aadd9/E
6fr
Emaj7(no3)
7fr
Aadd9
5fr
Badd4
7fr
Piano fills ad lib.

UNPRETTY

Words and Music by
DALLAS AUSTIN and
TIONNE TENESE WATKINS

* *Vocal line is written an octave higher than sung.*

* Vocal line is written as sung.

F/A G C G/B C/G F F/A G
cause of you. I try dif - f'rent ways but it's all the same. At the
C G/D C/B F/A G
end of the day I have my - self to blame. I'm just trip - pin'.
I have my - self to blame. Be - lieve I'm trip - pin'.
C G/B C/G F F/A G
You can buy your hair if it won't grow. You can fix your nose if he says so.
C G/D C/B F/A G
You can buy all the make - up that man can make. But if

C
G/B
C/G
F
F/A
G
you can't look in - side you,
find out who am I, too.
C
G/D
C/B
1
F/A
G
C
G/B
C/G
Be in the po - si - tion to make me feel so damn un - pret - ty.
F
F/A
G
C
G/D
C/B
F/A
G
Yeah, I make you feel un - pret - ty, too.
2
F/A
G
C
G/B
C/G
feel so damn un - pret - ty.
You can buy your hair if it won't grow.

F F/A G C G/D C/B
You can fix your nose if he says so. You can buy all the make - up the
F/A G C G/B C/G F F/A G
man can make. But if you can't look in - side you, find out who am I, too.
To Coda
C G/D C/B F/A G C G/B C/G
Be in the po - si - tion to make me feel so damn un - pret - ty.
F F/A G C G/D C/B
I make you feel un - pret - ty, too.

F/A
G
C
G/B
C/G
I make you feel un - pret - ty.
F
F/A
G
C
G/D
C/B
F/A
G
C
G/B
C/G
F
F/A
G
Oh.
Oh, oh.
C
G/D
C/B
F/A
G
C
G/B
C/G
F
F/A
G
Oh.
Oh, oh.
Oh.
Oh, oh.

D.S. al Coda
C G/D C/B F/A G
Oh. Oh, oh.
CODA
C G/B C/G
You can buy your hair if it won't grow.
F F/A G
C G/D C/B
You can buy all the make - up that
F/A G
man can make.
C G/B C/G
But if you can't look in - side you.
F F/A G
C G/D C/B F/A
Be in the po - si - tion to make me feel so.
Repeat and Fade
G
Optional Ending
C

YOUR EYES

Words and Music by MICK HUCKNALL

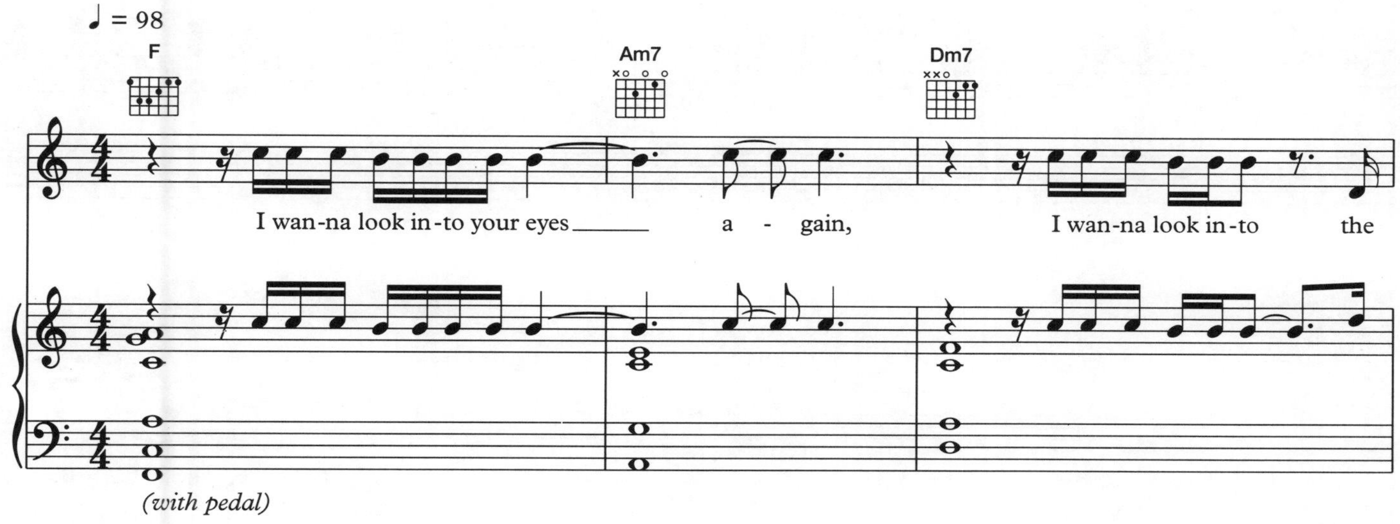

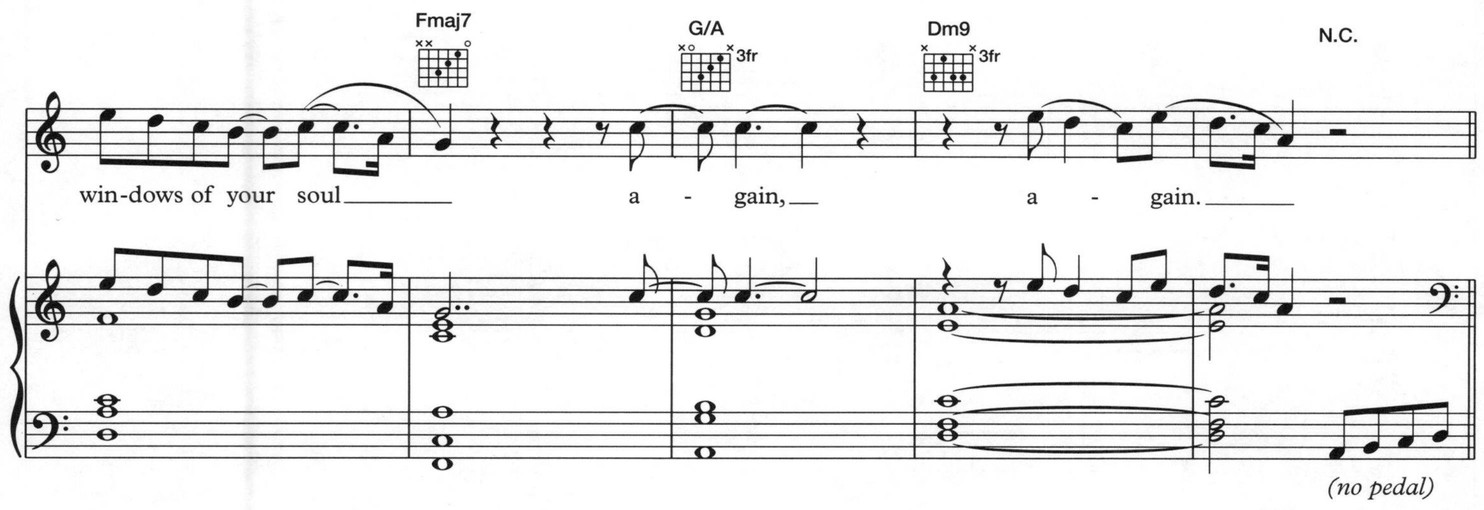

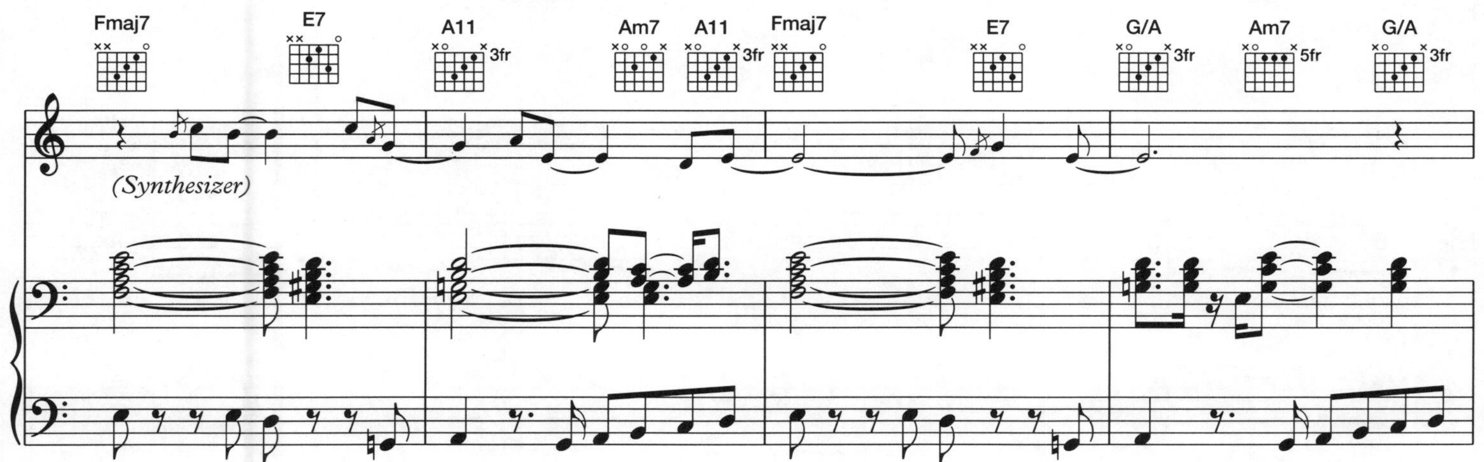

Fmaj7
E7
A11
Am7
A11
Fmaj7
E7
G/A
Am7
G/A
Dm9
E7
A11
Dm9
E7
1. Who's to know where time will lead us now? I can't be-lieve this is
G/A
Am7
G/A
Dm9
E7
hap-pen-ing now. I'm not scared, I'm just
A11
Am7
A11
Dm9
E7
G/A
Am7
G/A
won-der-ing how, I wan-na see your eyes.

Dm9 E7 A11 Dm9 E7
2. All the time we shared be - tween us now, feel - ing I have needs me to
G/A Dm9 E7
make a vow. Now as I leave I must re -
A11 Am7 A11 Dm9 E7 G/A Am7 G/A
- turn some - how, 'cause I wan-na see your eyes.
Fmaj7 E7 A11 Am7 A11 Fmaj7 E7
I wan-na look in - to your eyes a - gain, I wan-na look in - to the

G/A
Fmaj7
E7
A11
Am7
A11
Fmaj7
E7
3fr
win-dows of your soul, a - gain, a - gain.
G/A
Am7
5fr
N.C.
When I look at you I fum-ble, my con-fi-dence takes a tum-ble. But when I
look in-to your eyes I just crum-ble 'cause I know that it's you that my heart burns
for, that it's you that I'm yearn - ing for, well.

Fmaj7
E7
A11
Am7
A11
Fmaj7
E7
3fr
I wan-na look in-to your eyes a - gain,
I wan-na look in-to the
G/A
Fmaj7
E7
A11
Am7
A11
win-dows of your soul, - - a - gain,
Fmaj7
E7
G/A
Am7
G/A
Fmaj7
E7
A11
Am7
A11
5fr
a - gain.
Look in-to your eyes,
Fmaj7
E7
G/A
Am7
G/A
Fmaj7
E7
look in - to your eyes,
look in - to your eyes,

to Coda
A11
Am7
A11
Fmaj7
E7
G/A
Am7
G/A
look in - to your eyes.
Who's
Dm9
E7
A11
Dm9
E7
to know where time will lead us now?
I can't be - lieve this is
G/A
Am7
G/A
Dm9
E7
hap - pen - ing now.
Well I'm not scared, I'm just
A11
Am7
A11
Dm9
E7
G/A
Am7
G/A
won - der - ing how,
I wan - na see your eyes.

D.𝄋 al Coda
CODA
Dm9
E7
G/A
3fr
Am7
5fr
G/A
3fr
I __ wan-na make __ it right. __
G/A
3fr
Am7
5fr
G/A
3fr
Fmaj7
E7
A11
3fr
Am7
A11
3fr
Look in - to your eyes, __
Fmaj7
E7
G/A
3fr
Am7
5fr
G/A
3fr
Fmaj7
E7
look in - to your eyes, __
look in - to your eyes, __
repeat to fade
A11
3fr
Am7
A11
3fr
Fmaj7
E7
G/A
3fr
Am7
5fr
G/A
3fr
look in - to your eyes. __

WAR OF NERVES

Words and Music by CAMERON McVEY,
MAGNUS FIENNES, SHAZNAY LEWIS,
MELANIE BLATT, NATALIE APPLETON
and NICOLE APPLETON

G
G7
C
-ware of your des-ti-ny. When that mo-ment ar-
B♭9
C
B♭9
-rives, world vi-sions through the mind and
C
B♭9
G
G7
all I see is what used to be, my life could soon be a mem-o-ry.
E♭
fr3
C
F
I don't ev-er want to feel pain, I wan-na be rea-dy when you

C
E♭
fr3
C
call my name. I don't ev - ver want to feel fear, 'cause
D9
fr4
1.
G
ev - 'ry night feels al-right when you're near.
2.
Gsus4
G
A♭maj7
A♭maj7/B♭
fr3
near. Don't wan-na be like a voice with-out
C
A♭maj7
A♭maj7/B♭
fr3
words. Don't wan - na be a - lone in this

C
B♭add9
A♭maj7
B♭6/7
world
and will I win
this war of
C
Fm/C
C
Fm/C
nerves.
C
Fm/C
G7(♭9)
G
G7
G7aug
G7
B
E♭
C
F9
I don't ev - er want to feel pain,
I wan-na be rea - dy when you
(2. 3. see block lyric)

Verse 2:
Battle through this war of nerves
When your life, it takes a turn
And what I have is what I fear
While in my mind you're lying here.
Feel that unholy dread
There's a piece of me in all he says
All kinds of mixed-up inside my head
This stage fright in my own bed.

At B final choruses:
2
I don't ever want to feel pain
When it's over, will I feel the same?
I don't ever want to feel fear
This war of nerves that I reserve
For when you're here.

3
I don't ever want to feel pain
I'm feeling hurt but I feel no shame
I don't ever want to feel fear
Do I deserve these cruel words
We have here?

Printed and bound in Great Britain 6/00